Monet The Early Years

Before impressionist painter Claude Monet painted the famous flowers and water lilies from his garden, he created the paintings in this coloring book. These paintings, usually filled with people (often his family or friends) rather than flowers, are from Monet's early years.

Monet helped found the impressionist movement, which used quick brush strokes to capture fleeting moments in time. But this didn't happen right away. An artist's style tends to grow and change over the years, and these paintings show us how Monet developed his art, how he became the revolutionary artist known around the world today.

A selection of paintings from the exhibition *Monet: The Early Years* are shown in this coloring book. His original artworks are shown on the insides of the front and back cover. You can use those images for reference, or you can color the images based on your own impressions. Feel free to use the extra pages we've included at the back to experiment and develop your own signature style.

All works are by Claude Monet (French, 1840–1926).

1. *Houses on the Bank of the River Zaan*, 1871/1872. Oil on canvas, 47.5 x 73.5 cm (18¹¹⁄₁₆ x 28¹⁵⁄₁₆ in.). Städel Museum, Frankfurt. Photograph © Städel Museum - U. Edelmann - ARTOTHEK

2. *The Beach at Trouville*, 1870. Oil on canvas, 54 x 64.8 cm (21¼ x 25½ in.). Wadsworth Atheneum Museum of Art, Hartford, Connecticut. The Ella Gallup Sumner and Mary Catlin Sumner Collection Fund, 1948.116. Photograph courtesy Allen Phillips / Wadsworth Atheneum

3. *The Pont Neuf*, 1871. Oil on canvas, 53.3 x 73 cm (21 x 28¾ in.). Dallas Museum of Art. The Wendy and Emery Reves Collection, 1985.R.38. Photograph courtesy Dallas Museum of Art

4. *The Red Kerchief*, c. 1868–1873. Oil on fabric, 99 x 79.8 cm (38¹⁵⁄₁₆ x 31⅜ in.). The Cleveland Museum of Art. Bequest of Leonard C. Hanna Jr., 1958.39

5. *Regatta at Argenteuil*, c. 1872. Oil on canvas, 48 x 75 cm (18⅞ x 29½ in.). Musée d'Orsay, Paris. RF2778. © RMN-Grand Palais / Art Resource, NY. Photograph by Hervé Lewandowski

6. *Still Life with Flowers and Fruit*, 1869. Oil on canvas, 100.3 x 81.3 cm (39½ x 32 in.). The J. Paul Getty Museum, Los Angeles. Digital image courtesy of the Getty's Open Content Program

7. *The Cradle – Camille with the Artist's Son Jean*, 1867. Oil on canvas, 116.2 x 88.8 cm (45¾ x 34¹⁵⁄₁₆ in.). National Gallery of Art, Washington. Collection of Mr. and Mrs. Paul Mellon, 1983.1.25

8. *Interior, after Dinner*, 1868/1869. Oil on canvas, 50.2 x 65.4 cm (19¾ x 25¾ in.). National Gallery of Art, Washington. Collection of Mr. and Mrs. Paul Mellon, 1983.1.26

9. *Sailboats on the Seine at Petit-Gennevilliers*, 1874. Oil on canvas, 54 x 65 cm (21¼ x 25⅝ in.). Fine Arts Museums of San Francisco. Gift of Bruno and Sadie Adriani, 1962.23

10. *Luncheon on the Grass*, center panel, 1865–1866. Oil on canvas, 248 x 217 cm (97⅝ x 85⁷⁄₁₆ in.). Musée d'Orsay, Paris. Inv. RF1987-12. © RMN-Grand Palais / Art Resource, NY

11. *Camille on the Beach in Trouville*, 1870. Oil on canvas, 38.1 x 46.4 cm (15 x 18¼ in.). Yale University Art Gallery, New Haven, Connecticut. Collection of Mr. and Mrs. John Hay Whitney, B.A. 1926, Hon. 1956, 1998.46.1

12. *Farmyard in Normandy*, c. 1863. Oil on canvas, 65 x 81.3 cm (25⁹⁄₁₆ x 32 in.) Musée d'Orsay, Paris. RF3703. © RMN-Grand Palais / Art Resource, NY

13. *On the Beach at Trouville*, 1870–1871. Oil on canvas, 38 cm x 46 cm (14¹⁵⁄₁₆ x 18⅛ in.). Musée Marmottan Monet, Paris. Erich Lessing / Art Resource, NY

14. *Luncheon on the Grass*, left panel, 1865–1866. Oil on canvas, 418 x 150 cm (164⁹⁄₁₆ x 59¹⁄₁₆ in.). Musée d'Orsay, Paris. RF1957-7. © RMN-Grand Palais / Art Resource, NY. Photograph by Patrice Schmidt

15. *Meditation (Madame Monet on the Sofa)*, c. 1871. Oil on canvas, 48 x 75 cm (18⅞ x 29½ in.). Musée d'Orsay, Paris. RF3665. © RMN-Grand Palais / Art Resource, NY. Photograph by Gérard Blot

16. *On the Bank of the Seine, Bennecourt*, 1868. Oil on canvas, 81.5 x 100.7 cm (32¹⁄₁₆ x 39⅝ in.). The Art Institute of Chicago. Potter Palmer Collection, 1922.427. Photograph courtesy Bridgeman Images

17. *Still Life with Melon*, c. 1872. Oil on canvas, 53 x 73 cm (20⅞ x 28¾ in.). Museu Calouste Gulbenkian, Lisbon. The Calouste Gulbenkian Foundation. Inv. 450. © The Calouste Gulbenkian Foundation / Scala / Art Resource, NY. Photograph by Catarina Gomes Ferreira

18. *The Artist's Son*, 1868. Oil on canvas, 42.5 x 50 cm (16¾ x 19¹¹⁄₁₆ in.). Ny Carlsberg Glyptotek, Copenhagen. Photograph by Ole Haupt

19. *The Landing Stage*, 1871. Oil on canvas, 54 x 74 cm (21¼ x 29⅛ in.). Private collection

20. *Springtime*, c. 1872. Oil on canvas, 50 x 65.5 cm (19¹¹⁄₁₆ x 25¹³⁄₁₆ in.). The Walters Art Museum, Baltimore, Maryland. Acquired by Henry Walters, 1903 (37.11). thewalters.org

21. *Seascape, Storm*, 1866. Oil on canvas, 48.7 x 64.6 cm (19³⁄₁₆ x 25⁷⁄₁₆ in.). Sterling and Francine Clark Art Institute, Williamstown, Massachusetts. 1955.561. Image © Sterling and Francine Clark Art Institute, Williamstown, Massachusetts. Photograph by Michael Agee

• •

Pomegranate Communications, Inc.
19018 NE Portal Way, Portland OR 97230
800 227 1428   www.pomegranate.com
Pomegranate's mission is to invigorate, illuminate, and inspire through art.

Distributed by Pomegranate Europe Ltd.
'number three', Siskin Drive, Middlemarch Business Park
Coventry CV3 4FJ, UK
+44 (0)24 7621 4461   sales@pomeurope.co.uk

© 2016 Pomegranate Communications, Inc.

Item No. CB188

Designed by Carey Hall

Printed in Korea

25 24 23 22 21 20 19 18 17 16   10 9 8 7 6 5 4 3 2 1

1. *Houses on the Bank of the River Zaan, 1871/1872*

2. *The Beach at Trouville, 1870*

3. *The Pont Neuf, 1871*

4. *The Red Kerchief,* c. 1868–1873

5. Regatta at Argenteuil, c. 1872

6. *Still Life with Flowers and Fruit, 1869*

7. The Cradle – Camille with the Artist's Son Jean, 1867

8. *Interior, after Dinner*, 1868/1869

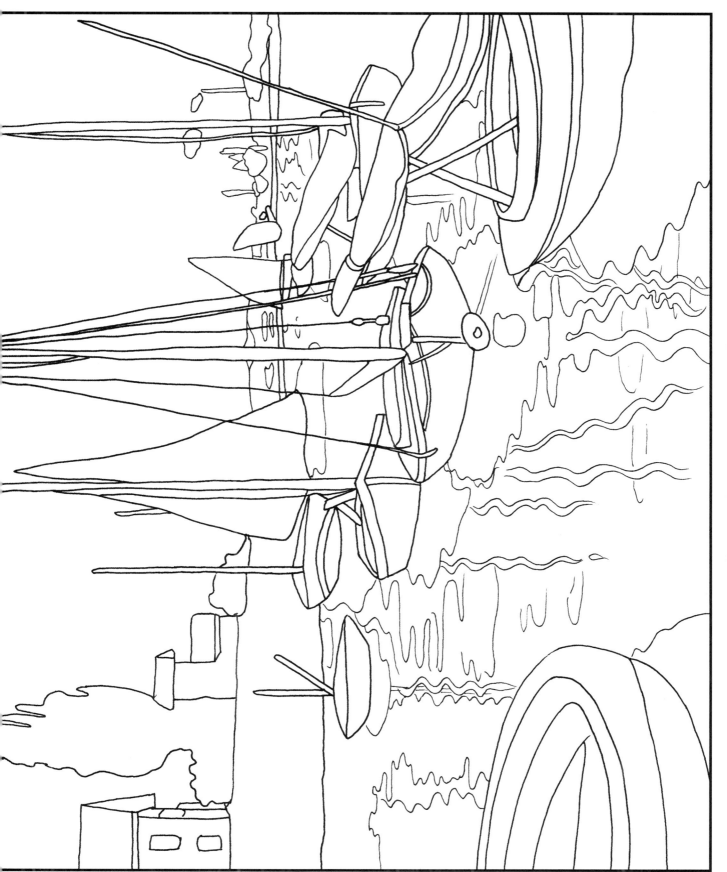

9. *Sailboats on the Seine at Petit-Gennevilliers, 1874*

10. *Luncheon on the Grass*, center panel, 1865–1866

11. *Camille on the Beach in Trouville*, 1870

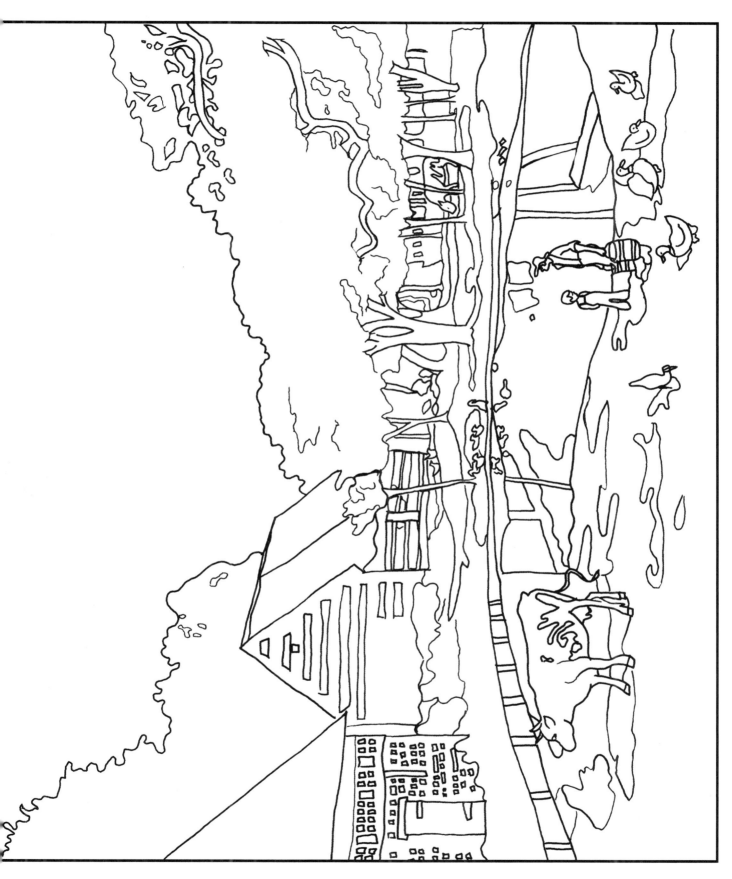

12. *Farmyard in Normandy,* c. 1863

13. On the Beach at Trouville, 1870-1871

14. *Luncheon on the Grass*, left panel, 1865–1866

15. *Meditation (Madame Monet on the Sofa)*, c. 1871

16. On the Bank of the Seine, Bennecourt, 1868

17. *Still Life with Melon*, c. 1872

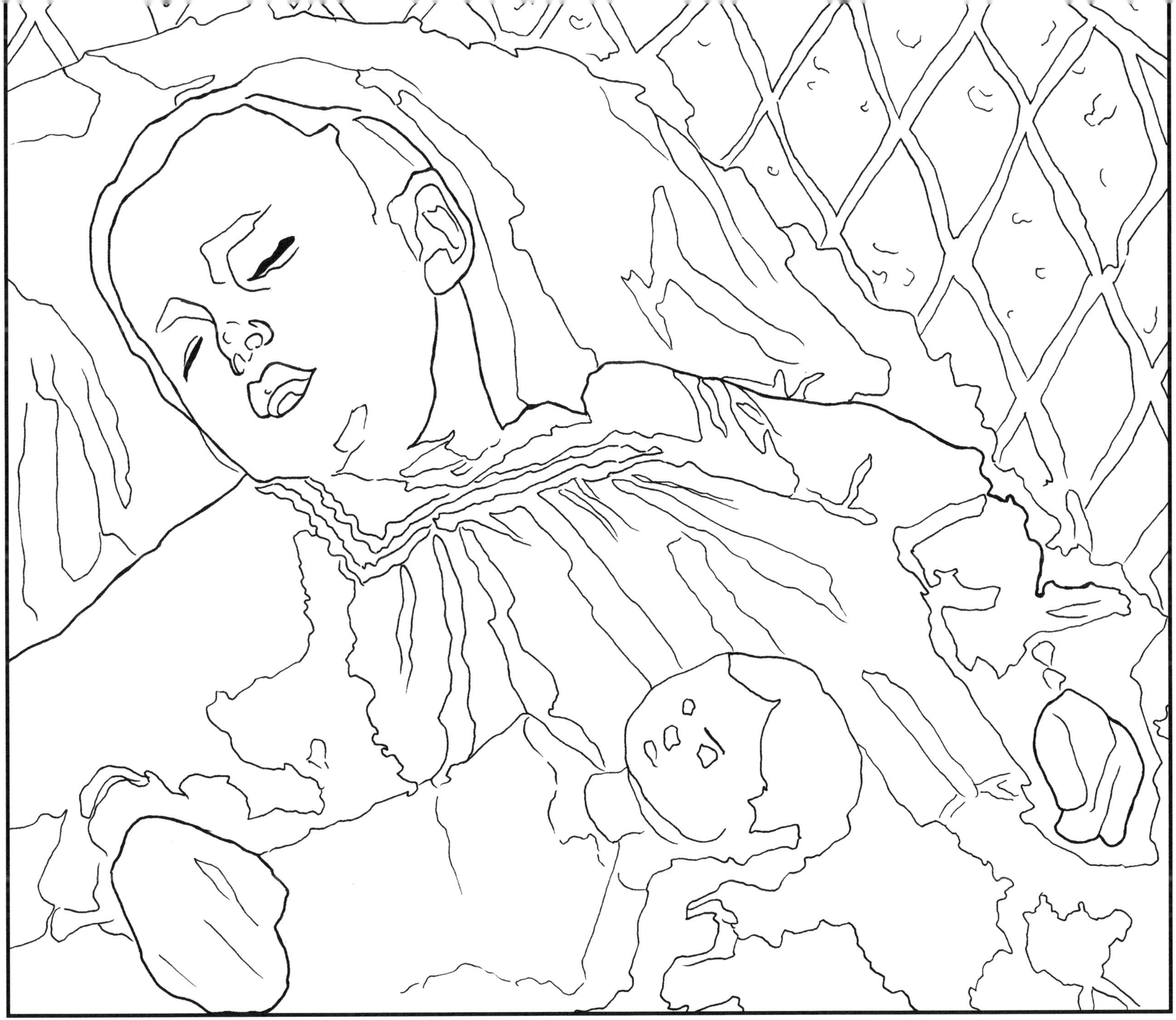

18. *The Artist's Son*, 1868

19. The Landing Stage, 1871

20. *Springtime, c. 1872*

21. *Seascape, Storm*, 1866

Draw and color your own picture here!

Draw and color your own picture here!